SHRIMP
CRAB FARMING

**A Symbiotic Approach To
Aquaculture Success**

**Harness The Benefits Of Shrimp
And Crab Co-Culture For
Increased Productivity And
Profits**

Dr. Fernando Florence

1

Table of Contents

CHAPTER ONE

Overview Of Shrimp And Crab Farming

Shrimp and crab farming are vital segments of the aquaculture industry, making considerable contributions to global seafood output and economic development. These crustaceans are highly regarded for their culinary appeal and nutritional worth, making them in-demand commodities in both local and international markets.

Shrimp and crab farming operations range in size and intensity, from tiny, family-run businesses to big commercial operations.

Environmental conditions, water quality management, disease control, and market demand all have a significant impact on shrimp and crab farming profitability.

History Of Shrimp And Crab Farming

Shrimp and crab farming has a centuries-long history, with evidence of traditional aquaculture activities in ancient civilizations such as China, Egypt, and Greece. Shrimp and crab farming was traditionally done in coastal ponds, rice paddies, and tidal flats.

Aquaculture technology and practices have advanced throughout time, including selective breeding, pond management, and feed formulation, transforming shrimp and crab farming into a complex and financially successful sector. Shrimp and crab farms may now be found in nations all over the globe, creating jobs and boosting local economies.

Current Trends In Shrimp And Crab Farming

Several significant trends shape the shrimp and crab farming sector, reflecting shifts in customer tastes, technical improvements, and market dynamics. One significant trend is an increase in demand for sustainably produced marine products, which is being driven by environmental and food safety concerns. As a consequence, there is an increased interest in certification systems and labeling schemes that encourage ethical aquaculture methods.

Furthermore, advances in genetics, nutrition, and disease control have resulted in increases in production efficiency, disease resistance, and product quality.

Benefits Of Shrimp And Crab Farming

Shrimp and crab cultivation provides several advantages to both producers and consumers. From a producer's standpoint, growing these crustaceans offers a consistent source of revenue, job possibilities, and economic growth, especially in rural and coastal regions. Shrimp and crab aquaculture also helps to improve food security by boosting the availability of high-quality protein-rich seafood items in local and international markets. Farmed shrimp and crabs provide customers with a continuous supply of fresh, healthy, and economical seafood, decreasing dependence on wild-caught fisheries and encouraging sustainable food production techniques.

Challenges Of Shrimp And Crab Farming

Despite its many advantages, shrimp and crab farming has several obstacles that must be solved for it to be sustainable and profitable over time.

Disease outbreaks are one of the most serious issues, since they may decimate shrimp and crab populations and cause considerable economic losses for producers.

Diseases including white spot syndrome virus (WSSV), infectious hypodermal and hematopoietic necrosis virus (IHHNV), and hepatopancreatic microsporidiosis (HPM) are among the most prevalent dangers to shrimp and crab farms. Other issues include environmental deterioration, habitat loss, pollution, and regulatory limits.

Objectives Of Shrimp And Crab Farming

Shrimp and crab farming aims to create high-quality seafood products in a sustainable and ecologically responsible way. This involves increasing production efficiency, lowering resource consumption, and mitigating harmful effects on adjacent ecosystems.

Furthermore, shrimp and crab farming strives to help rural and coastal communities by providing revenue, offering job opportunities, and supporting local businesses. Shrimp and crab farming may help to improve food security, economic growth, and environmental sustainability by supporting ethical aquaculture techniques.

CHAPTER TWO

Site Selection And Preparation.

Site selection and planning are critical aspects in launching a successful shrimp and crab farming company.

The selection of an acceptable location requires careful consideration of several criteria, including water quality, soil properties, terrain, accessibility, and environmental restrictions.

Ideally, the location should have access to clean, high-quality water sources with appropriate salt levels, enough room to build a pond or tank, and enough drainage to avoid floods. To reduce environmental dangers, the location should be positioned distant from polluting sources such as industrial operations or agricultural runoff.

Once a good location has been located, it must be carefully prepared to provide ideal growth conditions for shrimp and crabs. This may include clearing land, leveling the ground, and building ponds or tanks by certain design specifications.

Pond construction is critical for preserving water quality, controlling sedimentation, and promoting water exchange. Adequate infrastructure, including water delivery systems, aeration devices, and fencing, should also be provided to support farm operations and maintain biosecurity.

Stocking Density And Species Selection

Stocking density and species selection are critical factors in influencing the productivity and profitability of a shrimp and crab farming enterprise.

Stocking density is the number of individuals supplied per unit area on a farm and is determined by variables like as water quality, pond size, management strategies, and species-specific needs. Overstocking may cause overcrowding, greater competition for resources, and a higher incidence of illnesses while understocking can result in the underutilization of pond areas and lower production yields.

Species selection is also crucial since various shrimp and crab species have varying growth rates, nutritional needs, environmental tolerances, and market preferences.

Pacific white shrimp (Litopenaeus vannamei), black tiger shrimp (Penaeus monodon), and freshwater prawns (Macrobrachium spp.) are among the most commonly grown shrimp species, while mud crab (Scylla serrata) and blue swimming crab (Portunus pelagicus) are popular crab species. Species selection should take into account local environmental variables, market demand, and agricultural aims.

Food And Nutrition Management

Feeding and nutrition management are key parts of shrimp and crab aquaculture since they have a direct impact on growth performance, health, and production efficiency.

Proper nutrition is critical for satisfying shrimp and crabs' dietary needs, supporting healthy development, and reducing the danger of nutritional deficiencies and illnesses. Commercially prepared feeds are widely used in shrimp and crab aquaculture to provide critical nutrients, vitamins, and minerals for growth and development. These feeds are available in a variety of formats, including pellets, granules, and powders, and are designed to suit the nutritional requirements of shrimp and crabs at various life stages.

Water Quality Management

Water quality control is critical in shrimp and crab farming to generate and maintain ideal growth conditions for these crustaceans. Temperature, dissolved oxygen, pH, salinity, ammonia, nitrite, and nitrate levels are some of the most important water quality metrics to monitor and control. Proper water quality management is critical for encouraging healthy development, decreasing stress, preventing disease outbreaks, and increasing output yields.

To maintain ideal conditions in the agricultural environment, management measures such as water exchange, aeration, filtration, and frequent monitoring of water quality indicators are used.

CHAPTER THREE

Harvesting And Processing Techniques

Harvesting and processing processes are key phases in producing high-quality shrimp and crab items for the market.

Harvesting is the process of removing adult shrimp and crabs from the aquaculture environment using proper procedures and equipment to reduce stress and harm. Seining, trapping, and netting are common harvesting techniques, depending on the species and agricultural system. To maintain product quality, freshness, and safety, shrimp and crabs may be processed in a variety of ways after harvesting, including sorting, grading, washing, chilling, and packing.

Proper handling and processing processes assist shrimp and crab products retain their taste, texture, and nutritional content while increasing their market appeal and shelf life. Furthermore, processing facilities must follow high food safety and sanitation standards to avoid contamination and comply with regulatory regulations.

To summarize, site selection and preparation, stocking density and species selection, feeding and nutrition management, water quality control, and harvesting and processing processes are all critical components of successful shrimp and crab farming.

By following best practices in these areas, shrimp and crab growers may increase production, profitability, and sustainability while fulfilling the rising demand for high-quality seafood products.

Growth Performance Of Shrimp And Crab

The growth performance of shrimp and crab is an important aspect in determining the viability and profitability of aquaculture operations. Growth rates have a direct influence on crop yields, time to market, and total economic returns for farmers. Several variables impact shrimp and crab development performance, including genetics, ambient conditions, water quality, feed quality, stocking density, and management approaches.

Shrimp and crab growth rates vary according to species, age, and environmental factors. Warm water temperatures, suitable dissolved oxygen levels, optimum salinity levels, and high-quality feed are all factors that contribute to optimal shrimp and crab development.

Proper feeding management, frequent monitoring of water quality indicators, and efficient disease control techniques are all critical for encouraging healthy development and increasing output yields.

Environmental Impacts

Shrimp and crab aquaculture may have a major environmental effect on nearby ecosystems, especially if not managed responsibly.

Common environmental hazards linked with shrimp and crab production include habitat destruction, pollution, biodiversity loss, and water nutrient enrichment.

Intensive shrimp and crab farming techniques, such as high stocking densities, overuse of feed and fertilizers, and poor waste management, may cause water quality deterioration, sedimentation, and eutrophication.

These environmental consequences may injure aquatic animals, affect ecosystem function, and decrease water quality, endangering both aquatic and human health.

Risk Assessment And Management Strategies

Risk assessment and management are critical components of responsible shrimp and crab farming techniques that seek to reduce

24

possible negative effects on the environment, human health, and farm production. Identifying possible hazards, assessing their probability and severity, and putting suitable risk-mitigation measures in place are all components of effective risk assessment.

Common dangers linked with shrimp and crab production include disease outbreaks, water pollution, habitat degradation, and regulatory noncompliance. Implementing biosecurity measures to avoid disease introduction and spread, adopting environmentally friendly agricultural techniques, and adhering to appropriate legislation and certification requirements are all possible risk management options.

Best Practices For Shrimp And Crab Farming

Implementing best practices in shrimp and crab farming is critical for fostering sustainable aquaculture operations, reducing environmental effects, and producing safe and high-quality seafood products.

Best practices include several facets of farm management, such as integrated pest management, disease prevention and control techniques, and regulatory compliance and certification.

CHAPTER FOUR

Integrated Pest Management

Integrated pest management (IPM) is a comprehensive strategy for pest control that seeks to limit the usage of chemical pesticides and environmental impact while efficiently controlling pest populations.

IPM tactics for shrimp and crab aquaculture may involve habitat alteration, biological control measures, cultural practices, and pest outbreak monitoring and early detection.

Disease Prevention And Control Measures

Disease prevention and management are key components of shrimp and crab farming operations since they reduce the likelihood of disease outbreaks and their influence on farm output.

Disease prevention strategies may involve stringent biosecurity policies, screening and quarantining incoming stock, ensuring ideal water quality conditions, and giving a balanced diet to boost immune function.

In addition, immunization, probiotic supplementation, and the use of immune-stimulating chemicals may improve disease resistance in shrimp and crabs. Disease control procedures may include the use of antimicrobial agents, cleaning of equipment and buildings, and the removal and disposal of diseased personnel to avoid disease transmission on the farm.

Regulatory Compliance And Certification

Regulatory compliance and certification are required to ensure that shrimp and crab farming operations follow local, national, and international norms and laws controlling food safety, environmental protection, and animal welfare. Compliance with regulatory regulations helps companies reduce legal risks, preserve public confidence, and get access to local and foreign markets.

Certification schemes such as the Aquaculture Stewardship Council (ASC) and Best Aquaculture Practices (BAP) provide third-party verification of shrimp and crab farming practices, ensuring that farms adhere to strict environmental sustainability, social responsibility, and product quality standards.

Certification signifies a commitment to ethical aquaculture methods, which may improve market access and customer trust in shrimp and crab products.

Finally, responsible shrimp and crab farming practices must consider growth performance, environmental impacts, risk assessment and management strategies, integrated pest management, disease prevention and control measures, and regulatory compliance and certification.

Shrimp and crab farmers may decrease environmental effects, mitigate risks, and maintain the long-term sustainability and profitability of their operations by following best practices and adopting sustainable management techniques.

Successful Shrimp And Crab Farming Operations

Successful shrimp and crab farming operations serve as examples of excellence in the aquaculture business, displaying profitability, sustainability, and social responsibility.

These enterprises have achieved high levels of productivity, efficiency, and environmental stewardship by using effective management techniques, technology advancements, and strategic decision-making.

Lessons From Failed Attempts

Despite the potential for success, many shrimp and crab farming enterprises have faced obstacles and ultimately failed to meet their goals. These failures teach the industry crucial lessons about the significance of rigorous planning, risk management, and adapting to changing circumstances. Disease outbreaks, environmental deterioration, poor management methods, and insufficient market access are among the most common causes of failure.

CHAPTER FIVE

Future Directions And Innovations

The future of shrimp and crab aquaculture is driven by continuous technology breakthroughs, market trends, and environmental factors.

Aquaculture technological innovations, such as automated feeding systems, recirculating aquaculture systems (RAS), and genetic modification programs, are projected to increase production efficiency, minimize environmental impact, and improve product quality. Furthermore, developing market prospects, such as rising demand for organic and sustainably produced seafood, may stimulate diversification and growth in the shrimp and crab farming business.

Technological Progress In Shrimp And Crab Farming

Technological improvements are critical in encouraging innovation and increasing the efficiency and sustainability of shrimp and crab farming operations. Farmers can maximize production results, cut costs, and limit environmental consequences thanks to advances in genetics, nutrition, disease control, and water quality monitoring. For example, developing disease-resistant shrimp and crab strains may help reduce the danger of disease outbreaks, while precision aquaculture technologies enable real-time monitoring and management of environmental conditions.

Potential For Growth And Diversification

Market demand, regulatory restrictions, resource availability, and technical innovation all have an impact on the shrimp and crab farming industry's capacity to expand and diversify. While conventional shrimp and crab farming operations in coastal regions rely on monoculture production, there is an increasing interest in investigating alternate production techniques and species diversity. For example, inland aquaculture systems like as RAS and integrated multi-trophic aquaculture (IMTA) provide prospects for the long-term extension and diversification of shrimp and crab farming operations.

Research Needs And Opportunities.

Continued research and innovation are required to meet the difficulties and possibilities confronting the shrimp and crab farming business. Disease prevention and control, genetic enhancement, environmental sustainability, and market growth are among the key study fields. Investing in research and cooperation among academia, business, and government agencies may help the shrimp and crab farming sector overcome current limits, capitalize on upcoming possibilities, and contribute to the aquaculture industry's long-term development and resilience.

Conclusion

Finally, successful shrimp and crab farming businesses serve as examples of excellence in the aquaculture sector, displaying profitability, sustainability, and social responsibility. However, the sector confronts many obstacles, including disease outbreaks, environmental deterioration, and market instability. By learning from previous mistakes, adopting technological improvements, and investing in research and innovation, the shrimp and crab farming sector can capitalize on upcoming possibilities and contribute to the aquaculture industry's long-term growth and resilience.

Implications For The Aquaculture Industry

The success of shrimp and crab farming operations has significant consequences for the whole aquaculture business. As global seafood demand rises, sustainable growth and diversity of shrimp and crab farms may help satisfy it while putting less strain on wild fish supplies. Furthermore, effective shrimp and crab farming operations may serve as examples of best practices in other aquaculture industries, encouraging environmental stewardship, social responsibility, and economic growth.

Recommendations To Practitioners And Policymakers

To ensure the shrimp and crab farming industry's development and sustainability, practitioners and politicians should prioritize investments in research and innovation, reinforce regulatory frameworks, and encourage stakeholder engagement.

Furthermore, measures to expand market access, infrastructure, and capacity-building programs may assist shrimp and crab farming reach its full potential as a source of sustainable seafood production and economic growth.

Working together, practitioners and policymakers may create a climate conducive to the shrimp and crab farming industry's sustained success and expansion.

Made in the USA
Columbia, SC
16 July 2024